KU-106-666

TABLE OF CONTENTS

Meet the "Mega Robo Bros"

News // UK // Technology // Robotics

13 August
by V. Chandra, staff writer

On a quiet residential street near Stepney Green in East London, something extraordinary is happening. Because one of these unassuming terraced houses is home to Alex and Freddy Sharma – two primary school-age brothers who argue over all the usual brother stuff, who play video games and love ice cream and hanging out with their friends. And who also happen to be the most sophisticated robots in the country, or indeed possibly the world.

No-one's quite sure on that last point – in part because so few reporters have been given access to the boys. Their adopted mother is the world-renowned cyberneticist Doctor Nita Sharma, Chief Scientific Officer of R.A.I.D., and she guards their privacy fiercely. I've been granted a rare interview today, but when I arrive at their door I can't help but feel Dr Sharma is eyeing me suspiciously; her manner is very quiet and reserved.

Freddy's, on the other hand, is less so. I enter the living room to find him charging around with a pair of bright purple underpants on his head, yelling "EAT YOUR OWN BUTTOCKS, MAN!" with what can only be described as full-throated glee.

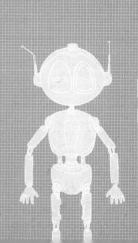

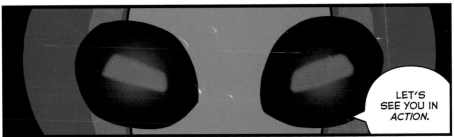

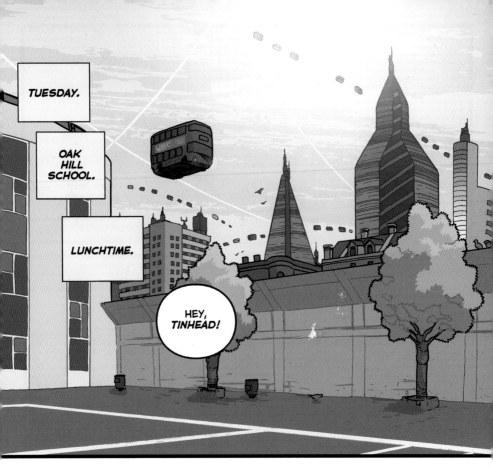

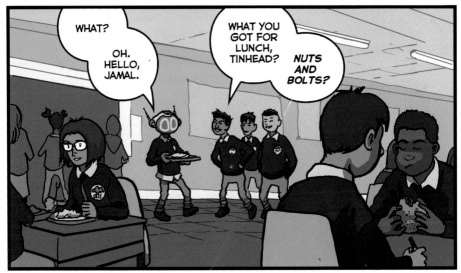

17

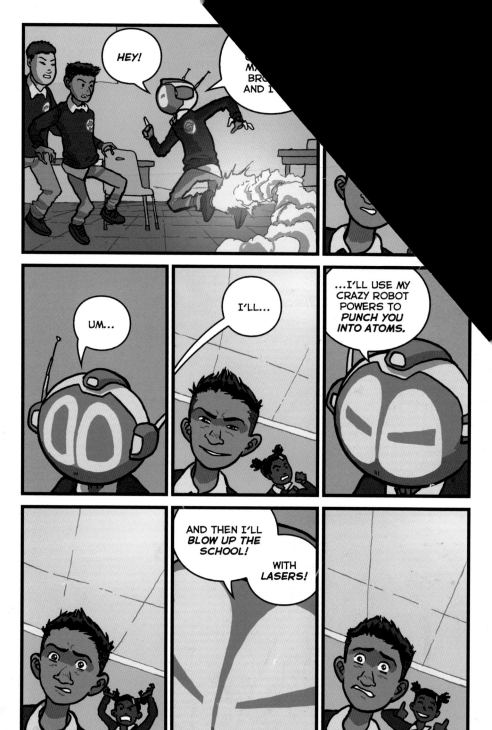

21

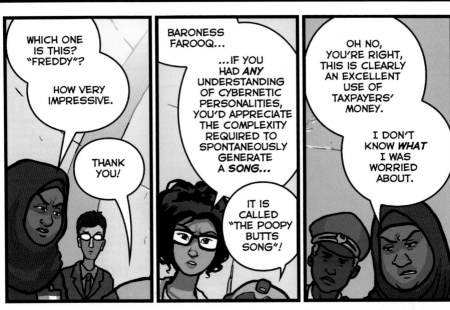

24

THEY HAVE *CANDY FLOSS!*

I ACTUALLY THOUGHT COMING HERE WOULD HELP ME EXPLAIN SOMETHING.

YOU REMEMBER HOW WE'VE TALKED ABOUT *SENTIENCE* – WHAT MAKES YOU GUYS DIFFERENT FROM OTHER ROBOTS?

UM... YEAH?

THIS PLACE – THE *WORLD* – IS FULL OF ROBOTS

AND SOME OF THEM CAN TALK – CAN EVEN HAVE CONVERSATIONS, SORT OF.

Howdy, little pardner!

Try your luck in the OLD WEST SHOOTOUT?

BUT THEY'RE NOT SENTIENT. THEY'RE NOT *THINKING*, NOT REALLY.

THEY JUST HAVE DATA-BANKS OF SET WORDS AND PHRASES, AND PROGRAMMED RULES FOR HOW TO COMBINE THEM.

29

FWOOOOSH!!

WAS THAT FREDDY?

STOP!

COME BACK!

YOU'RE NOT ALLOWED TO DO THAT!

YEP, THAT WAS FREDDY.

SIGH.

ALEX, WOULD YOU MIND?

SURE, MUM.

HOLD ON.

32

FRIDAY.

BEDTIME.

GUYS?

HAVE YOU CLEANED YOUR FILTERS?

YES, MUM!

ALL RIGHT. I'LL SAY NIGHT NIGHT, THEN.

NIGHT, MUM.

DAD! CAN WE HAVE A *FIGHT?*

NOT NOW, FREDDY, NO.

COME ON, INTO BED.

34

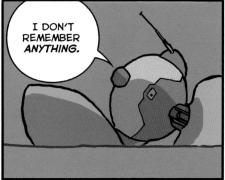

CHAPTER 2

44

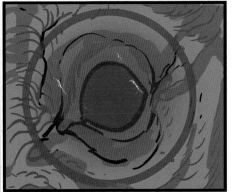

47

FRIDAY NIGHT.

ARE YOU SURE YOU'LL BE OK, SUSIE?

I'M *FINE*, NITA.

GO! HONESTLY, WHEN WAS THE LAST TIME YOU GUYS HAD A NIGHT OUT?

I CAN'T EVEN REMEMBER. I THINK I WAS CLEAN-SHAVEN.

REMEMBER, ANY PROBLEMS AT ALL, JUST CALL!

JUST GO!

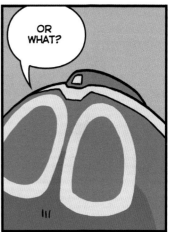

CHAPTER

3

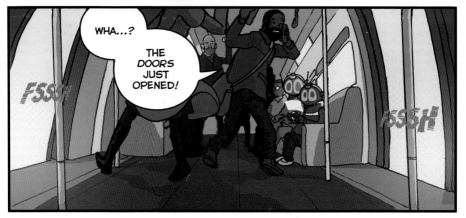

74

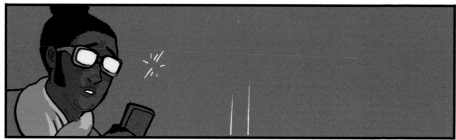

CHAPTER
4

...SEE WHAT I MEAN?

LIKE FREDDY ON HIS OWN WASN'T ANNOYING ENOUGH, NOW HE'S GOT HIS TRICERATOPS DOG, HIS INSANE GORILLA AND HIS... *STUPID PHILOSOPHY PENGUIN.*

AND IT'S LIKE THIS *ALL DAY.*

ALL RIGHT, MR GRUMPYPANTS.

...SORRY.

I'M JUST *TIRED.* I DIDN'T GET MUCH SLEEP.

ARE YOU OKAY, ALEX?

YEAH. JUST...

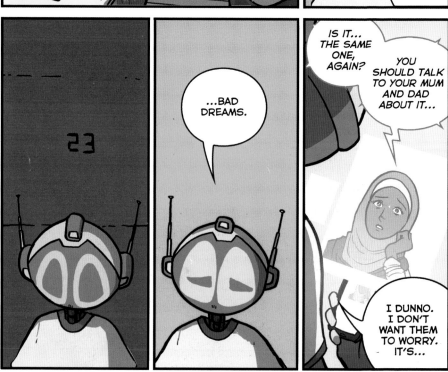

23

...BAD DREAMS.

IS IT... THE SAME ONE, AGAIN?

YOU SHOULD TALK TO YOUR MUM AND DAD ABOUT IT...

I DUNNO. I DON'T WANT THEM TO WORRY. IT'S...

DOCTOR SHARMA? A WORD, PLEASE.

IN PRIVATE.

BOYS, YOU...

...JUST PLAY FOR A MINUTE, OKAY?

OKAY, GUYS! ROBO DEATH BALL!

TWO TEAMS! DRONES VERSUS SUPER MEGA AWESOME SQUAD!

(THAT'S US, TRIKEY!)

MEGA ROBO HEARING.

...A FULL DELTA CODE SHUTDOWN?! DO YOU HAVE ANY IDEA THE TROUBLE...

WITH RESPECT, BARONESS FAROOQ, I DIDN'T HAVE A CHOICE!

THEY WERE ABOUT TO BE ALL OVER EVERY FEED IN THE COUNTRY!

DOCTOR SHARMA... YOUR IMPULSE TO PROTECT YOUR BOYS IS COMMENDABLE.

BUT IT MAY BE A LUXURY WE CAN NO LONGER AFFORD.

A SPY-EYE TRAWL CAUGHT FOOTAGE OF THE ATTACKER LEAVING THE SCENE AFTER THE SKYLINE INCIDENT.

WE HAVE A POSITIVE I.D.

WAS IT...?

ROBOT 23.

WE'RE PULLING ALL TRACES FROM THE MUSEUM AND THE SHOPPING CENTRE INCIDENTS. IT LOOKS LIKE...

CHAPTER
5

THIS IS TOTALLY BORING.

CAN I GET AN ICE CREAM?

UM... GRAN?

ARE YOU SURE WE'RE SUPPOSED TO BE HERE?

OF COURSE!

YOUR FATHER ASKED ME TO LOOK AFTER YOU BOYS TODAY, DIDN'T HE?

YEAH, BUT...

I THINK HE THOUGHT WE WERE MORE JUST, Y'KNOW, GOING TO HANG OUT AT YOUR HOUSE AND PLAY BOARDGAMES AND STUFF?

WELL THEN, THIS IS A *FUN SURPRISE* FOR YOU!

IT IS PRINCE EUSTACE'S BIRTHDAY! A CELEBRATION!

WHERE *ELSE* WOULD WE BE?

I LIKE THE BIG ROBOTS.

I GUESS.

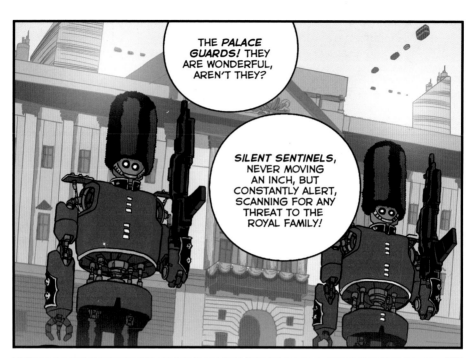

THE *PALACE GUARDS!* THEY ARE WONDERFUL, AREN'T THEY?

SILENT SENTINELS, NEVER MOVING AN INCH, BUT CONSTANTLY ALERT, SCANNING FOR ANY THREAT TO THE ROYAL FAMILY!

I DON'T REALLY *GET* THE ROYAL FAMILY.

WHAT'S THE BIG DEAL? THEY'RE JUST... *POSH PEOPLE.*

WHA – *?!*

HOW ARE YOUR PARENTS *RAISING* YOU?

OH, THEY ARE TOO YOUNG, YOUR MOTHER AND FATHER. THEY HAVE *NEVER* APPRECIATED WHAT IT...

WAIT! LOOK! THEY'RE COMING OUT!

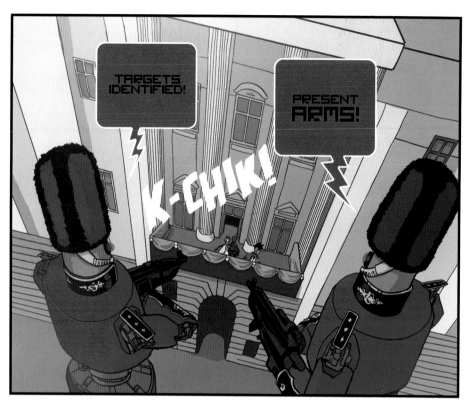

115

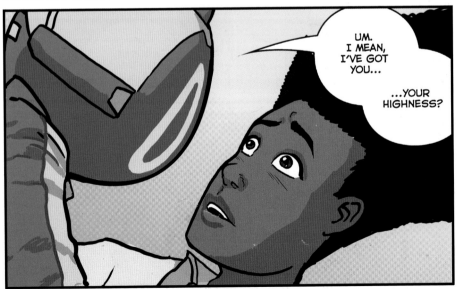

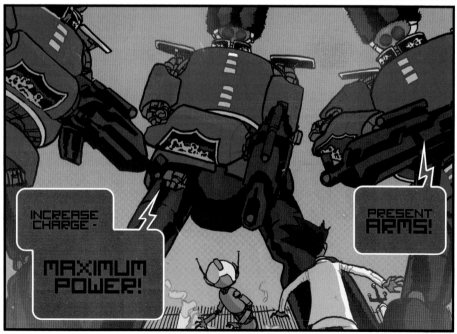

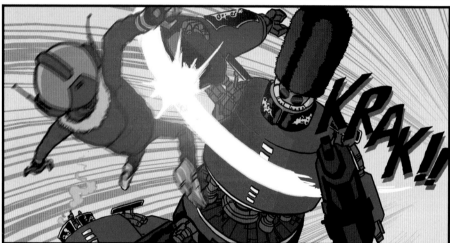

CHAPTER 6

OH, HEY, WE'RE AT THE PLAYROOM.

TWO MILES IN UNDER A MINUTE! PRETTY COOL, RIGHT?

I THINK I'M GOING TO BE SICK...

MONSIEUR GORILLA! STUPID PHILOSOPHY PENGUIN! I MISSED YOU GUYS!

"God is absence. God is the solitude of man."

CROISSANT!

I CAN'T BELIEVE YOU BUILT US A SECRET GETAWAY MONORAIL.

HEY, I'M A MUM. BUILDING SECRET GETAWAY MONORAILS IS MY JOB.

NO, YOUR *JOB* IS YOUR JOB.

OH — BARONESS FAROOQ!

I HATE TO BREAK UP THIS DELIGHTFUL FAMILY MOMENT, BUT I NEED YOU TO JOIN ME UP HERE.

ALL OF YOU.

WE NEED TO TALK ABOUT *ALEX.*

A TRAWL OF THE PALACE FOOTAGE PICKED THIS UP: RIGHT THERE IN THE CROWD, ADMIRING ITS HANDI-WORK.

LAUGHING AT US.

THAT'S THE *GUY!*

I SAW HIM, AT THE *THING!*

ROBOT 23.

WHO...

WHO *IS* HE?

140

YOU'D BE BACKED UP ON MISSIONS BY A FULL TEAM OF AGENTS AND COMMANDO MECHS...

IS THAT SUSIE?

SHE'S OUR BABY-SITTER!

HI, ALEX! HI, FREDDY!

AGENT NICHOLS IS SCIENTIFIC ATTACHÉ TO THE FIELD TEAM. SHE'LL STILL BE BABY-SITTING YOU, IN A SENSE. THERE'LL JUST BE... MORE EXPLOSIONS.

SO WHAT DO YOU SAY, ALEX? ARE YOU READY TO BECOME AN *AGENT OF R.A.I.D.?*

ALEX...

I KNOW THIS IS A LOT TO TAKE IN. DON'T LET THEM PRESSURE YOU.

YOU DON'T HAVE TO DO *ANYTHING* YOU DON'T WANT TO.

ACTUALLY, I THINK YOU'LL FIND...

NO, IT'S FINE. I...

I WANT TO. TO HELP.

TO... FIND THAT GUY.

CHAPTER 7

147

152

YOU HAVE TO LET IT GO, FREDDY.

ALEX NEEDS TO CONCENTRATE WHEN HE'S WORKING.

YOU CAN'T BE ALWAYS... HASSLING HIM AND *HECKLING* HIM ON YOUR PRIVATE COM-LINK.

GOODNESS KNOWS, HE'S GOT ENOUGH TO DEAL WITH.

BUT THAT'S *IT!*

WHAT IF HE *CAN'T* DEAL WITH IT?

YOU KNOW WHAT HE'S LIKE.

IF I'M NOT THERE TO LOOK AFTER HIM...

WHAT IF HE GETS IN TROUBLE?

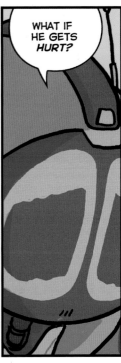

WHAT IF HE GETS *HURT?*

155

OW!

DAMMIT, FREDDY!

THAT REALLY...

SNFF

Y'KNOW...

DAD TOLD ME WHAT YOU SAID, AT THE PARK.

THAT YOU WORRY ABOUT ME.

PFF! WHY WOULD I WORRY ABOUT YOU?

YOU ARE A MORON WHO SMELLS LIKE BUTTS.

WELL, ANYWAY.

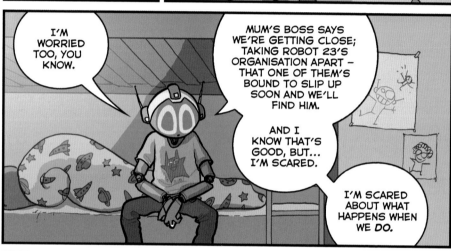

I'M WORRIED TOO, YOU KNOW.

MUM'S BOSS SAYS WE'RE GETTING CLOSE; TAKING ROBOT 23'S ORGANISATION APART – THAT ONE OF THEM'S BOUND TO SLIP UP SOON AND WE'LL FIND HIM.

AND I KNOW THAT'S GOOD, BUT... I'M SCARED.

I'M SCARED ABOUT WHAT HAPPENS WHEN WE DO.

THERE'S SOMETHING ABOUT THIS GUY, FREDDY.

I DON'T KNOW WHAT'S GOING TO HAPPEN.

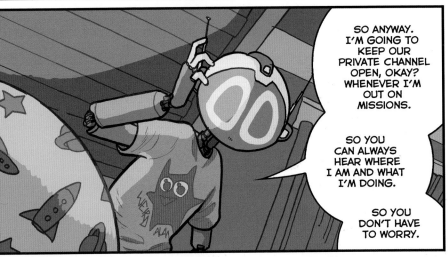

SO ANYWAY. I'M GOING TO KEEP OUR PRIVATE CHANNEL OPEN, OKAY? WHENEVER I'M OUT ON MISSIONS.

SO YOU CAN ALWAYS HEAR WHERE I AM AND WHAT I'M DOING.

SO YOU DON'T HAVE TO WORRY.

WASN'T WORRIED.

YOU WILL BE CAREFUL, THOUGH?

162

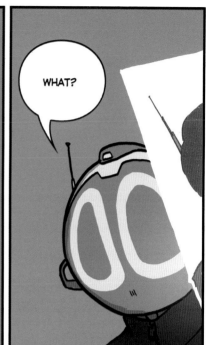

171

I KNOW HOW YOU *WORK*, YOU SEE.

I KNOW, BECAUSE WE'RE THE *SAME*.

WHO... *ARE* YOU?

YOU COULD SAY WE'RE RELATED.

I COME FROM THE SAME FACILITY THAT MADE YOU, *OBVIOUSLY*.

I MEAN, I'M CLEARLY A FAR SUPERIOR MODEL...

DON'T *MUMBLE*, DEAR BOY.

I *SAID*, YOU'RE *LYING!*

...

YOU *REALLY* DON'T REMEMBER?

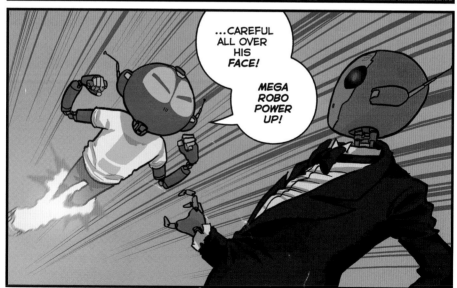

WEE-OOOOO

WEE-OOO

...NO CASUALTIES. INCREDIBLE.

NO *HUMAN* CASUALTIES, ANYWAY.

R.A.I.D.

APPARENTLY, ROBOT 23 HAD THE WHOLE TOP TEN FLOORS OF THE BUILDING, CONVERTED TO ITS... TO *HIS* PRIVATE BASE.

ALL THAT TIME, AND HE WAS RIGHT ON TOP OF US.

AND WE NEVER SUSPECTED A THING.

IT SEEMS HE HAD A WHOLE NETWORK OF DUMMY ACCOUNTS AND FAKE FRONT CORPORATIONS RENTING THE SPACE.

THAT... WAS ONE VERY CLEVER ROBOT.

BUT NOT AS CLEVER AS *ME* THOUGH, RIGHT?

DID HE SAY ANYTHING ELSE, ALEX?

ANYTHING THAT EXPLAINS WHY HE WAS... WHY HE WAS TRYING TO *DESTROY* YOU?

UM, NO.

NOT REALLY.

THE END

ALEX

ALEX WAS ALREADY FIVE WHEN HE CAME TO LIVE WITH THE SHARMAS, BUT DOESN'T REMEMBER MUCH OF HIS LIFE BEFORE. AND MAYBE... *DOESN'T WANT* TO REMEMBER.

STRENGTH	9
SPEED	9
WEAPONRY	9
SENTIENCE	9

FREDDY

FREDDY WAS ADOPTED BY MICHAEL AND NITA SHARMA WHEN HE WAS JUST A BABY, SO HE'S ONLY EVER KNOWN LIFE AS A KID IN A (RELATIVELY) NORMAL HOME!

STRENGTH	8
SPEED	9+
WEAPONRY	9+
SENTIENCE	9+

R.A.M
ROBOTICS AND
INTELLIGENCE &

DATA FI

MUM

ONE OF THE MOST BRILLIANT CYBERNETICISTS ON EARTH, DR NITA SHARMA IS THE SENIOR SCIENTIFIC OFFICER AT *R.A.I.D.** – AND ALEX AND FREDDY'S MUM!

STRENGTH	3
SPEED	5
WEAPONRY	3
SENTIENCE	9+

*R.A.I.D. STANDS FOR ROBOTICS ANALYSIS, INTELLIGENCE & DEFENCE

DAD

A FREELANCE SCIENCE JOURNALIST, MICHAEL MET NITA WHEN HE WAS COVERING HER WORK – LITTLE KNOWING THEY'D ONE DAY BE MARRIED WITH (ROBOT) KIDS!

STRENGTH	3
SPEED	5
WEAPONRY	3
SENTIENCE	9+

R.A.I.D
ROBOTICS ANALYSIS
INTELLIGENCE & DEFENCE

DATA FILES

THIS THEME PARK
ROBOT TRICERATOPS
DEVELOPED A FAULT,
AND NOW ACTS LIKE
IT'S A DOG!

OR POSSIBLY A CAT?
EITHER WAY, FREDDY
LOVES TRIKEY!

TRIKEY

STRENGTH	2
SPEED	5
WEAPONRY	3
SENTIENCE	3

LE GORILLE MÉCANIQUE
EST BRISÉ!

BAGUETTE!

MAUVAISES NOUILLES!

C'EST NETTEMENT
INUTILE.

STRENGTH	5
SPEED	4
WEAPONRY	2
SENTIENCE	2

MONSIEUR GORILLA

R.A.I.D

★ ROBOTICS ANALYSIS ★
INTELLIGENCE & DEFENCE

DATA FILES

STUPID PHILOSOPHY PENGUIN

"Life begins on the other side of despair."

DESIGNED TO DELIVER HELPFUL AND FRIENDLY INFORMATION TO THE PUBLIC, THIS ROBOTIC PENGUIN MALFUNCTIONED AND NOW...

...IS *LESS* HELPFUL.

STRENGTH	2
SPEED	5
WEAPONRY	3
SENTIENCE	3

ROBOT 23

LITTLE IS KNOWN ABOUT THE MYSTERIOUS *ROBOT 23* – HE CLAIMED TO BE A 'SUPERIOR MODEL' FROM THE SAME FACILITY WHERE ALEX AND FREDDY WERE BUILT.

STRENGTH	?
SPEED	?
WEAPONRY	?
SENTIENCE	?

HOW TO DRAW

1 OVAL SHAPE!

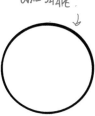

2

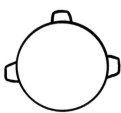

3 ANTENNAE!

4

5 FINISH OFF ANTENNAE!

6 DETAILS!

7

8 BIG BLUE EGG SHAPES!

9 DARKER BLUE EGG SHAPES INSIDE

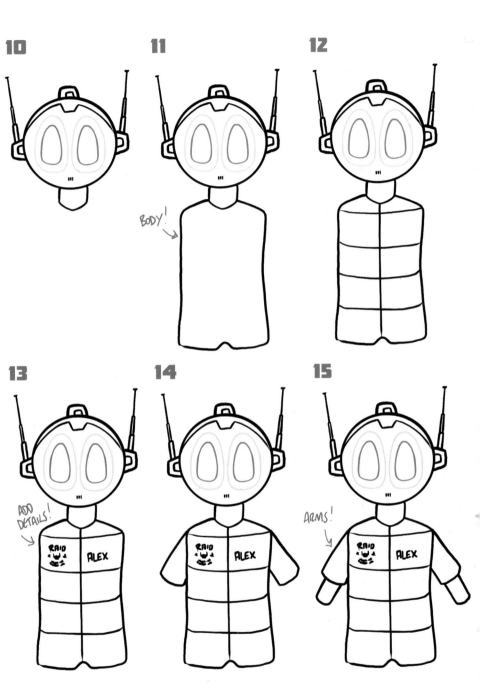

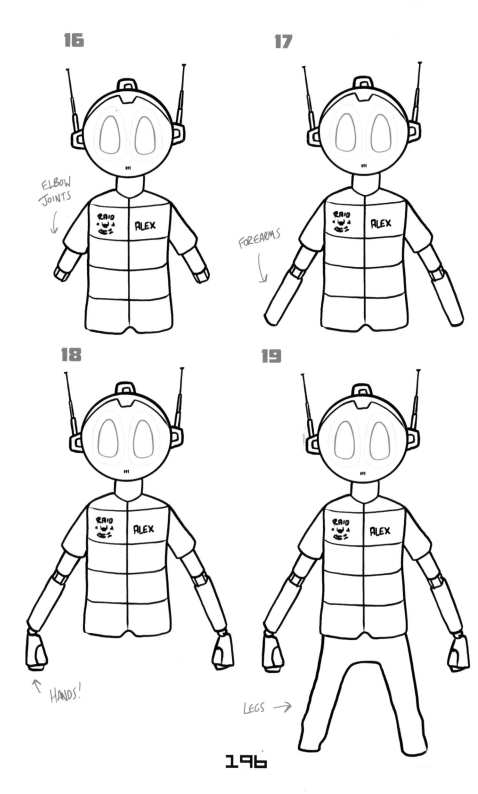

16

ELBOW
JOINTS

RAID
ALEX

17

FOREARMS

RAID
ALEX

18

RAID
ALEX

↑ HANDS!

19

RAID
ALEX

LEGS →

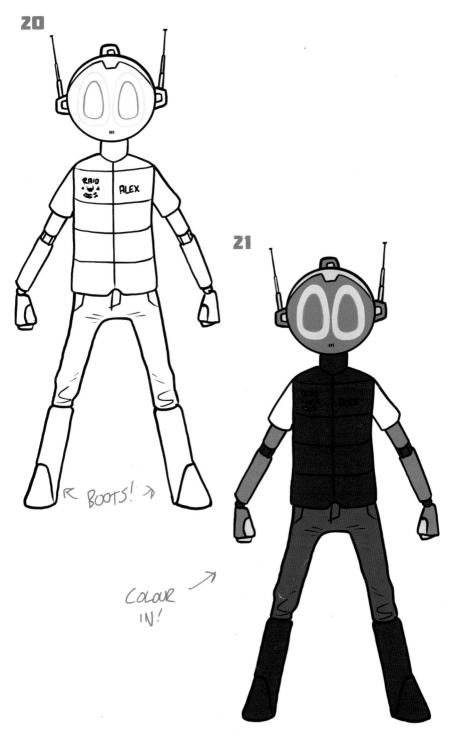

HOW TO DRAW Fredby

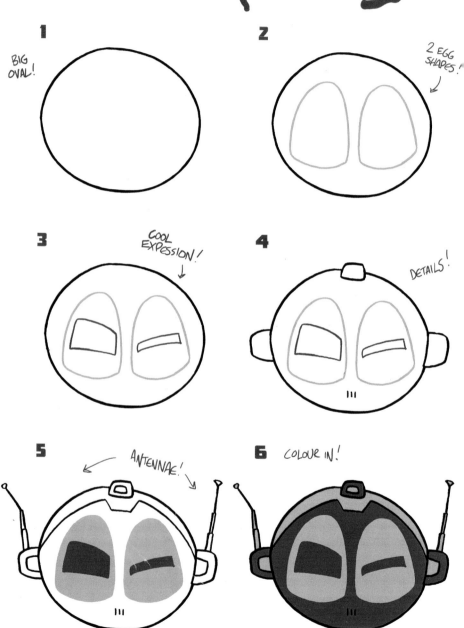

1 BIG OVAL!

2 2 EGG SHAPES!

3 COOL EXPRESSION!

4 DETAILS!

5 ANTENNAE!

6 COLOUR IN!

THE WORLD ACCORDING TO FREDDY!

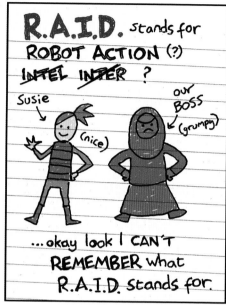

This story originally appeared in

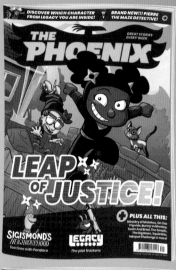

FREDDY VS SCHOOL & FREDDY AND THE NEW KID

MY NAME IS
FREDDY.
I LIVE WITH MY MUM & DAD.
I GO TO SCHOOL.
I'M AN
AWESOME ROBOT!

Okay humans, listen up! Here are the . . .

TOP 5 THINGS YOU SHOULD PROBABLY KNOW ABOUT ME!

1 My name is *FREDDY.*

2 I live in London with my mum and dad.

3 I go to school.

4 I have a big brother called Alex.

5 Oh yeah, the MAIN thing: I am an
AWESOME ROBOT!

. . . I should maybe have started with that?

I have many **AMAZING ROBOTIC ABILITIES**

I can . . .

FLY!

FWOOSH!!

And also I have

LASERS!

KZOW!

KZOW!

NEILL CAMERON is an award-winning writer and cartoonist. He is the creator of several comic books, including the *Mega Robo Bros* series, and *How to Make Awesome Comics.* Neill's comics appear regularly in The Phoenix, the weekly story comic. He has also written and illustrated two novels, *Freddy vs School*, and *Freddy and the New Kid.*

A+ Very well researched, Alex!

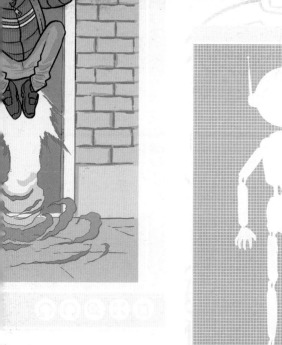

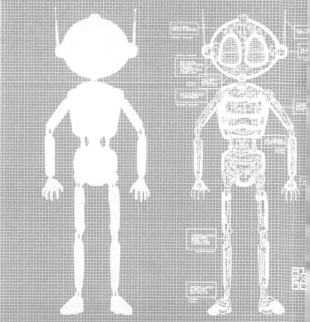

For Logan. Obviously.

Mega Robo Bros: Power Up
is a
DAVID FICKLING BOOK

First published in Great Britain in 2021 by
David Fickling Books,
31 Beaumont Street,
Oxford, OX1 2NP
www.davidficklingbooks.com

Text and illustrations © Neill Cameron, 2021
Cover design by Alison Gadsby, James Fraser and Paul Duffield.

978-1-78845-200-7
1 3 5 7 9 10 8 6 4 2

MIX
Paper from
responsible sources
FSC® C126477
www.fsc.org

DAVID FICKLING BOOKS Reg. No. 8340307
A CIP catalogue record for this book is available from the British Library.
Printed in Slovenia by Abografika.